RAIN DROP SPLASH

STORY BY ALVIN TRESSELT

PICTURES BY LEONARD WEISGARD

LOTHROP, LEE & SHEPARD BOOKS   NEW YORK

Text copyright © 1946, 1974 by Alvin Tresselt. Illustrations copyright © 1946, 1974 by Leonard Weisgard. All rights reserved. No part of this book may be reproduced or utilized in any form or by any means, electronic or mechanical, including photocopying and recording, or by any information storage and retrieval system, without permission in writing from the Publisher. Inquiries should be addressed to Lothrop, Lee & Shepard Books, a division of William Morrow & Company, Inc., 1350 Avenue of the Americas, New York, New York 10019. Printed in the United States of America.

First Edition 29 30 31 32 33 34 35 36 37 38

Drip drop splash,
drip drop splash,
drip drop splash
went the rain all day.

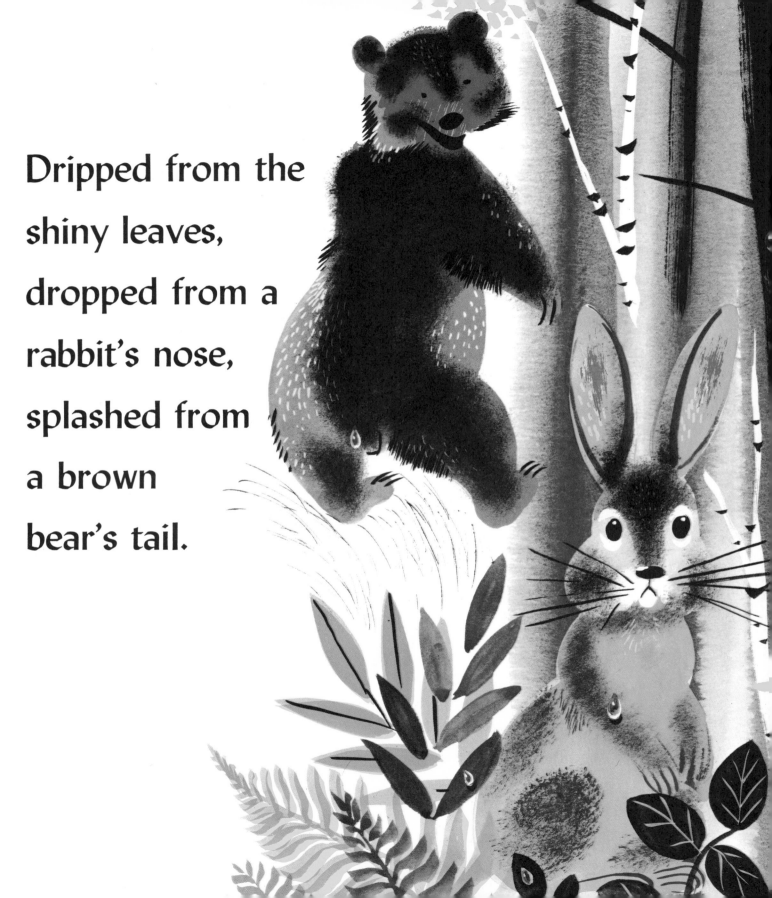

Dripped from the shiny leaves, dropped from a rabbit's nose, splashed from a brown bear's tail.

Fell from a
daisy's face,
trickled down
the tree trunks,
and splunked
on a green
frog's back.

There were so many rain drops
they made a puddle.
The puddle grew larger, and
larger, and larger, until it
became a pond. Water-lilies
floated on it, little fish
swam in it, and tiny snails
sat beside it.

Still it rained. Drip drop splash, drip drop splash, drip drop splash. The little pond grew larger and larger and spilled right over into a brook.

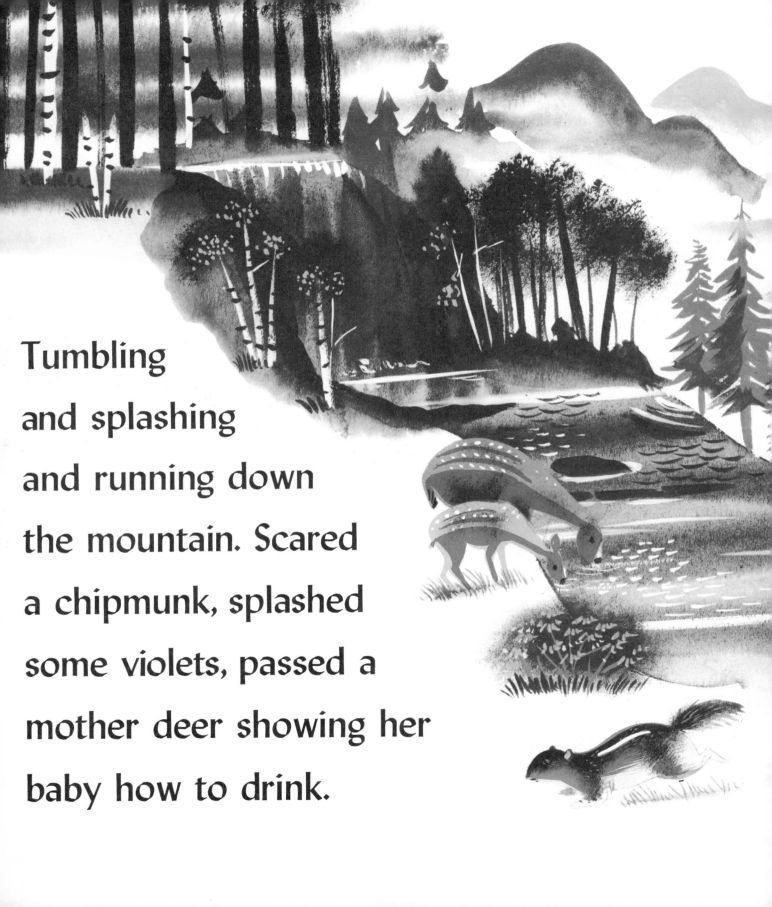

Tumbling
and splashing
and running down
the mountain. Scared
a chipmunk, splashed
some violets, passed a
mother deer showing her
baby how to drink.

Jumped over big stones, fell into deep pools, and rested on a bed of soft green moss. Then tumbled into a lake.

Now it was a big lake, with big fish and tall
pickerel weed. Dragonflies skimmed over

the water, turtles floated quietly, and a red winged blackbird built his nest in the rushes.

Still it rained. Drip drop splash,
drip drop splash, drip drop splash.
The lake grew larger and larger.
It flooded a farmer's meadow
and the cows stood in the mud.

It covered a road
and the cars couldn't pass
and the children
had to go to school in a boat.

Then it overflowed into a river,
with houses and towns along the
shore. It ran under bridges and

over waterfalls. Men fished
from the rocks, and two
teams had a boat race.

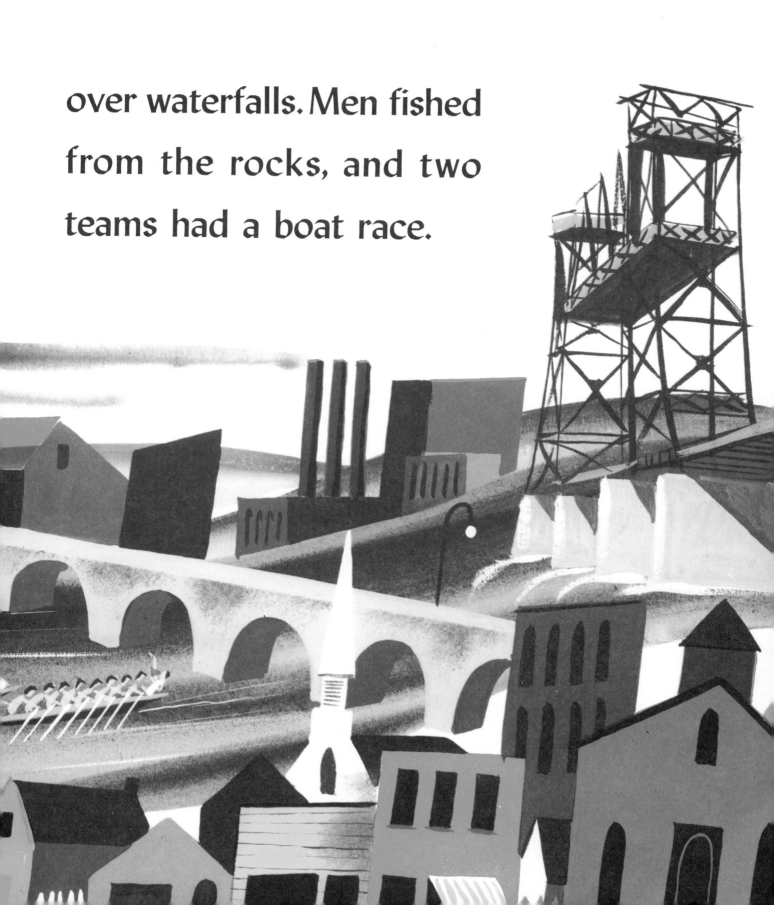

Past factories and warehouses, the river came to great cities with docks. There were ships and barges

and scows and tankers, and a
boatful of people
on a holiday.

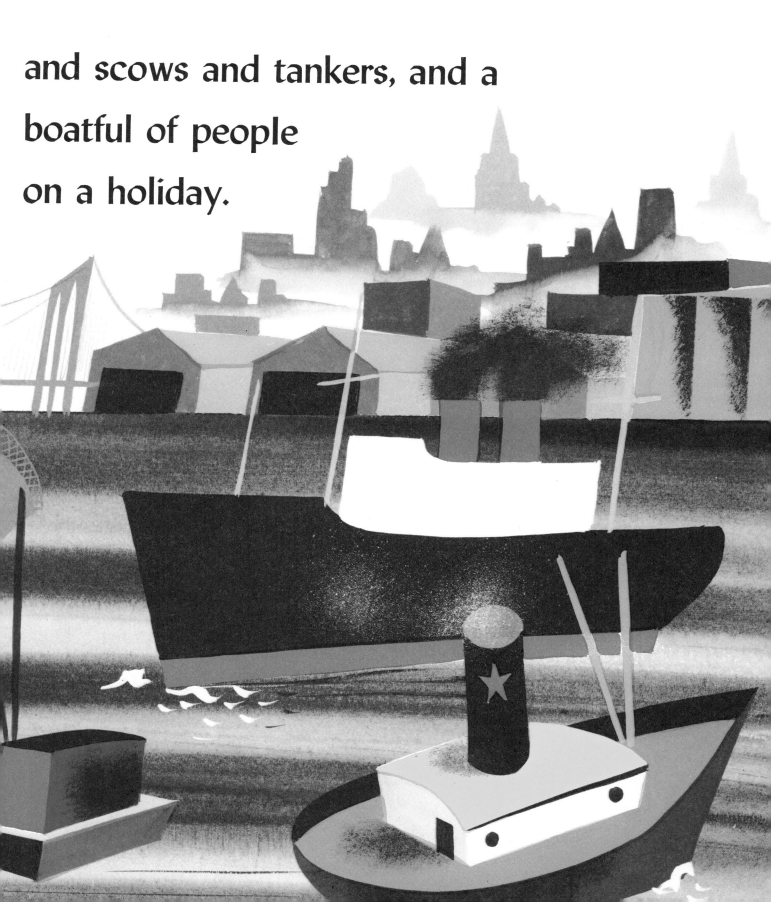

Little boys jumped into the water,
subway trains and cars
ran under it, ferry boats puffed
back and forth on top,
and seagulls flew over it
looking for fish to eat.

Then it passed a fort
and a lighthouse and a bell buoy,
and the river flowed into the sea.

Tall waves rolled up
to meet it.
There was an ocean liner
with lots of little tug boats
guiding it. The sun came out,
and at last the rain stopped.

A NOTE FROM THE AUTHOR

Rain Drop Splash started out as a mountain stream named Hyacinth, and I was going to follow her down the mountain until she eventually reached the sea. But somewhere along the journey this personified brook got hopelessly lost, and I realized that this approach to my story would never work. I decided to "tell it like it is"—to trace rain that falls on a mountainside and finally makes its way to the sea in a realistic manner, which turned *Rain Drop Splash* into a concept book, rather than a story of any kind. I managed to do this in less than five hundred words. The story was accepted for publication, and Leonard Weisgard was asked to illustrate it. This was my very first book for children, and it was named a Caldecott Medal Honor Book in 1946. As a result, countless children have learned about the natural progression of rainfall from brook to lake to river to sea, ever since.

—Alvin Tresselt